# Sally, where are you?

*Yvette Mintzberg*

**Heinemann : London**

Sally, where are you?

Sally?

# Sally, is that you?

Oh, Sally, you're a silly girl.

Sally?

# NOW, where's she gone?

My new nightgown!

Take that off at once!

Sally, are you playing games?

What are you doing with that
blanket on your head?

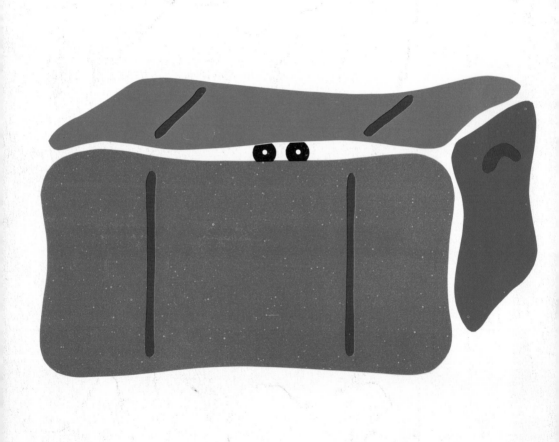

I don't believe it.
Sally, come out of that trunk.

THAT'S ENOUGH.

# SALLY!

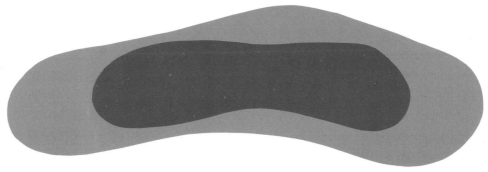

My goodness,
you don't have to cry
<u>that</u> much.

I know you were just playing,
but when I call you
I want you to come.

There, there.

Will a kiss make you
feel better?

Come, I've made some nice liver for lunch.

Sally?

# SALLY, WHERE ARE YOU?